At Home With Phonics

Jenny Roberts

with poems by

Cynthia Rider

Age
5–6

OXFORD

UNIVERSITY PRESS

About this book

Preparation for school

● At age 5-6, your child will be following the National Literacy Strategy in school.

● This book follows the same content as the National Literacy Strategy, and will give your child helpful preparation and practice in English.

Using the book

● Each double page spread focuses on a rhyming sound, for example '-an', or a phoneme, for example 's'. A phoneme is the smallest unit of sound in a word. There are approximately 44 phonemes in the English language, all of which your child will become familiar with during his or her primary years.

● Always enjoy the poem first, with your child. Talk about what happens in the poem and look at the picture.

● Then, identify the particular rhyming sound or phoneme in the poem, and encourage your child to write it by tracing over the pale letters.

● In each spread there are additional activities to reinforce your child's learning, which include drawing, colouring, identifying objects in a picture, repeating sounds and practising letter formation.

● In the middle of the book you'll find the tests: use each one to reinforce and practise the points taught in the book, and stick a gold star in the box on the activity page when the relevant test is completed.

● On page 32, there are apples which represent the worksheets. Encourage your child to colour them in as each worksheet is completed.

Helping your child

● Don't do too much at one sitting. One double page and its test is probably enough at a time for a child's concentration span.

● Practise reading and writing with your child at every opportunity: with food packets, public signs, or making shopping lists.

● Most important, give plenty of praise and encouragement. Learning always works best when based on success, fun and enjoyment!

NOW DO
TEST 1

OXFORD
UNIVERSITY PRESS

Great Clarendon Street, Oxford OX2 6DP

Oxford University Press is a department of the University of Oxford.

Oxford is a registered trade mark of Oxford University Press
in the UK and in certain other countries

© Jenny Roberts 2005
Edited and designed by Lodestone Publishing Limited, Uckfield, East Sussex
Illustrations by Jane Bottomley

The moral rights of the author have been asserted

Database right Oxford University Press (maker)

First published 2005
This edition 2007

British Library Cataloguing in Publication Data

Data available

ISBN-13: 978-0-19-838657-5

10 9 8 7 6 5 4 3 2 1

Printed in China

CONTENTS

Gran's Van

My old Gran
Has a tumbledown van.
It rattles along
Like an old tin can.
A man called Dan
Tried to mend Gran's van,
With a broken spanner
And a frying pan!

Cynthia Rider

Rhyming string – a n

v<u>an</u>

D<u>an</u>

c<u>an</u>

Gr<u>an</u>

p<u>an</u>

m<u>an</u>

Notes for Parents : **Activity focus: ending sound** *an* **What to do:**

- Read and enjoy the poem together, listening for the 'an' sound (as in 'van').
- Write over the pale letters, held by Gran, saying the sound 'an'.
- The adult reads the poem again, slowly and carefully, while the child listens for a word ending with the 'an' sound. When they hear the sound they can say so and the adult stops reading.

- Repeat the word together. Point to the relevant picture. The adult says the starting sound and the child says the ending sound 'an', then traces over the pale letters to complete the word. (Note, some words are repeated in the poem, but there is just one picture. Also, check that the child identifies 'man' with the picture of the man with the beard, rather than Dan.)

NOW DO
TEST 1

Ss

When Sally Sings a Sad Song

When Sally sings a sad song,
We all sing, too.
Sad songs make Sally sob,
So we sob, too.

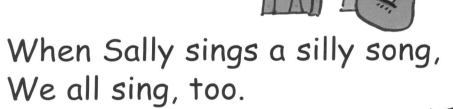

When Sally sings a silly song,
We all sing, too.
Silly songs make us laugh,
So Sally laughs, too.

Cynthia Rider

Initial phoneme – s

You will need:
coloured pens or pencils

Notes for Parents : **Activity focus:** s **What to do:**

- Read and enjoy the poem together, listening for the 's' sound (as in 'Sally').
- Write over the pale letters, in the snake, saying the sound.
- Look at the picture. Find and colour all the things beginning with 's' (sun, swing, slide, seat, spade,

sandpit, skipping rope, squirrel, Sally).
- Point to the pictures in turn. The child says the beginning sound of each word, and the adult says the rest of the word e.g. s-un, then say the whole word together.

NOW DO
TEST 2

7

M m

Mop It Up

Mop the mess up.
Mop, mop, mop.
Make it nice and clean.
Mop it up so Mum can't see
Where the mud has been.

Cynthia Rider

Initial phoneme – m

Notes for Parents : **Activity focus:** m **What to do:**

- Read and enjoy the poem together, listening for the 'm' sound (as in 'mop').
- Write over the pale letter 'm' on the monster's t-shirt, saying the sound.
- Talk about the messy monster in the picture. Point out that he has left muddy footprints behind him.
- Read the poem again, slowly and clearly, and ask

your child to listens out for any word beginning with 'm'. Whenever they hear this sound, they can tell you.
- The child writes an 'm' on one of the muddy prints (start by writing over the pale letters). Continue through the poem. (The words are mop, mess, mop, mop, mop, make, mop, Mum, mud.)

NOW DO
TEST 3

The Caterpillar Cake

Here comes Cathy
In a big cook's hat.
She's carrying a cake,
A caterpillar cake.
Six curly candles
And two currant eyes!
A caterpillar cake
For a birthday surprise!

Cynthia Rider

Initial phoneme – k / c

Notes for Parents : **Activity focus:** c **What to do:**

- Read and enjoy the poem together, listening for the 'c' sound (as in 'cake').
- Write over the pale letter 'c' on the card. Then write over the 'c's on the caterpillar's body, saying the sound.
- Together, make a collection of things beginning with the sound 'c'.

- Ask your child to draw them in the space above. (For example, a carrot, a candle, a cake, a cap, a cup, a cat, a can, a car.)
- Point to the objects in turn. The child says the beginning sound 'c'. Complete the rest of the word, e.g. c-arrot, then say the whole word together.

NOW DO
TEST 4

Tt

Tom the Tiger

Tom the tiger came to tea.
He ate some toast and jam.
He gobbled up ten treacle tarts
And a tin of tasty ham.
Tom the tiger looked at me
And said, "You do look sweet.
You'd make a tasty tit-bit
For a tiger's tea-time treat!"

Cynthia Rider

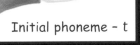

Initial phoneme – t

Notes for Parents : **Activity focus:** t **What to do:**

- Read and enjoy the poem together, listening for the 't' sound (as in 'Tom').
- Write over the pale letters on the banner, saying the sound.
- Look at all the things on the table. Ask your child to colour those beginning with 't'. (For example, TV,

teapot, teddy, tambourine, train and track, telephone, trousers.)

- Point to each item in turn. The child says the beginning sound 't'. Complete the word, e.g. t-eapot, then say the whole word together.

NOW DO
TEST 5

We're Going on a Goose Hunt

We're going on a goose hunt.
The goose has got away.
She isn't with the giddy goat.
He's gobbling up the hay.
She isn't in the garden
Or by the big green gate.
We've got to get the goose back
Because it's getting late.

Cynthia Rider

Initial phoneme – g

goat

girl

goal

_ate

_arden

_oose

Notes for Parents : Activity focus: g What to do:

- Read and enjoy the poem together, listening for the 'g' sound (as in 'goose').
- Write over the pale letter on the goose, saying the sound.
- Together, look at the pictures and say what they are.

- Ask your child to write in the missing letters.
- Point to the pictures in turn. The child says the beginning sound 'g'. Complete the word, e.g. g-oat, then say the whole word together.

NOW DO
TEST 6

Hurry, Harry, Hurry!

Hurry, Harry, Hurry!

Happy Harry Hare
Was hopping on his way,
When he saw a hungry fox
Hiding in the hay.

Harry had to hurry.
He hopped off all alone.
Hurry, Harry, Hurry!
Down the hill and home!

Cynthia Rider

Initial phoneme – h

At Home With Phonics

Age 5–6

Tests

OXFORD

UNIVERSITY PRESS

TEST 1

Complete the three rhyming words.

v_ _

Gr_ _

p_ _

TEST 2

Complete the words.

_ un

_ pade

_ wing

2

TEST 3

Match the words to the pictures.

mud

mop

Mum

TEST 4

Complete the words.

_up

_at

_ap

TEST 5

Match the words to the pictures.

teddy

tiger

train

TEST 6

Complete the words.

_ate

_irl

_oat

TEST 7

Colour the pictures of the words beginning with 'h'.

hen

house

tiger

horse

TEST 8

Match the words to the pictures.

bug

mug

jug

TEST 9

Complete the words.

so_ _

ki_ _

ne_ _

du_ _

TEST 10

Complete the words.

dre_ _

gra_ _

Je_ _

TEST 11

Match the words to the pictures.

lettuce

lamp

lemon

TEST 12

Colour the pictures of the words beginning with 'n' .

nest

apple

nuts

nine

ball

TEST 13

Match the words to the pictures.

dragon

dog

drum

TEST 14

Complete the words.

_ing

_ettle

_etchup

You will need:
coloured pens or pencils

Notes for Parents : **Activity focus:**   h   **What to do:**

- Read and enjoy the poem together, listening for the 'h' sound (as in 'Harry').
- Write over the pale letter 'h', saying the sound.
- Write an 'h' in each of the hares.
- Get your child to colour in anything in the picture that begins with 'h'. (For example, hares, horse, hay, home, helicopter, hen.)
- Look at each coloured picture, in turn. The child says the beginning sound 'h'. Complete the word, e.g. h-en, then say the whole word together.

NOW DO
TEST 7

Initial phoneme – h

17

The Hopping Bug

That bug is here.
That bug is there.
That bug is hopping everywhere.
It's on the rug.
It's on the jug.
It's hopped on top of Grandad's mug.
I would stop it if I could.
I would stop that hopping bug.

Cynthia Rider

Final phonemes – u g and o p

shop

jug

op
op
op

ug
ug
ug

Notes for Parents : **Activity focus: ending sounds   u g and   o p   What to do:**

• Read and enjoy the poem together, listening for the 'ug' sound at the end of words (as in 'bug') and the 'op' sound at the end of words (as in 'hop').

• Write over the pale letters 'ug' and 'op', saying the sounds.

• Read out the words on the word list and make sure your child listens very carefully, deciding whether each word

ends 'ug' or 'op'. If they think a word ends in 'ug' they write 'ug' on one line in the jug. If they think a word ends in 'op', they write 'op' on one line in the shop. The words on the list are: bug, hop, top, mug, rug, pop, slug, mop.

NOW DO
TEST 8

Final phonemes – u g and o p   **19**

Crack!

Crack! Crack!
Oh! What luck!
Here comes a tiny, baby duck.
A yellow back,
A yellow neck,
And a tiny beak to peck, peck, peck.

Cynthia Rider

Final phoneme – c k

sa   sack

du   du ck

so   so ck

     ck

ki   ki

ne   ne

NOW DO TEST 9

Notes for Parents : **Activity focus:** c k   **What to do:**

- Read and enjoy the poem together, listening for the 'ck' sound at the end of the words (as in 'crack').
- Write over the pale letters 'ck' on the egg, saying the sound.
- Together, look at the pictures, saying what they are.
- Ask your child to draw a line between the letters to make the word, then write the full word on the line.
- Point to the words in turn. Say the first sound and your child says the 'ck' sound at the end of the word, e.g. sa-ck, then say the whole word together.

Messy Jess

Baby Jess, what a mess!
Mud all over her best dress!
Runs across the wet, wet grass,
Trips and falls,
Then sits and bawls.
Who will kiss her?
Me I guess!
Come here, little baby Jess.

Cynthia Rider

Final phoneme – s s

ki_____

Te ss

Je_____

dre_____

gra ss

ss ss

Notes for Parents : **Activity focus:** s s   **What to do:**

- Read and enjoy the poem together, listening for the 'ss' sound (as in 'mess').
- Write over the pale letters 'ss' saying the sound.
- Together, look at the picture and talk about it (e.g. Baby Jess is crying because she fell on the grass. Her older sister, Tess, is giving her a kiss to cheer her up).

- Your child fills in the missing letters on the labels. (Jess, Tess, grass, dress, kiss)
- Point to the labels in turn. Say the first part of the word and ask your child to say the rest, e.g. Te-ss, then say the whole word together.

NOW DO
TEST 10

L l

Lucy's Lunch

Lucy Lion licks her lips
And says, "I'd like some lunch.
I'll just look in the larder
For a lettuce leaf to munch."
Lucy has no lettuce left.
She goes to Lily's shop.
She gets a lovely lettuce
And a lot of lollipops.

Cynthia Rider

Grapheme/phoneme correspondence – l

Lily's Shop

Notes for Parents : **Activity focus:** l **What to do:**

- Read and enjoy the poem together, listening for the 'l' sound (as in 'lunch').
- Write over the pale 'l' letters saying the sound.
- Talk about all the things you can see in the shop window.
- Ask the child to look for things beginning with 'l'. When they find something, they colour it in, and write one 'l'

on Lucy's list. (They should identify: lettuce, lemon, lunch box, lorry, lamp and lollipops.)
- Point to the items in turn. Your child says the beginning sound 'l' and you complete the word, e.g. l-ettuce.

NOW DO
TEST 11

N n

A Noisy Din

What a nasty noise!
What a noisy din!
Nine naughty kittens
Are banging on a tin.
Nine naughty puppies
Are running to join in.
What a nasty noise!
What a noisy din!

Cynthia Rider

Grapheme/phoneme correspondence – n

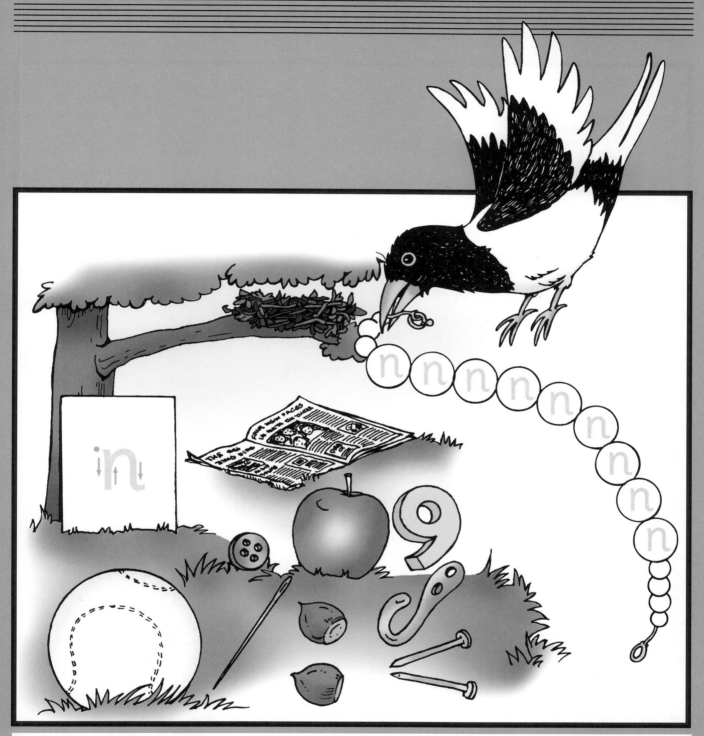

Notes for Parents : **Activity focus:** n **What to do:**

- Read and enjoy the poem together, listening for the 'n' sound (as in 'noise').
- Together, look at the picture. Your child writes over the large pale 'n' saying the sound.
- Point to the nest and ask your child what it is. Explain that the nest belongs to a magpie, who loves collecting things beginning with the sound 'n'. She has already found a necklace.

- Ask your child to write over the pale 'n's in the necklace.
- Look at the things below. Which things would the magpie like in her nest? Your child should draw a line between the objects and the nest: nuts, nail, needle, number nine, newspaper.
- Point to each object in turn. Your child says the beginning sound 'n'. Complete the word, e.g. n-uts.

NOW DO
TEST 12

Dd

Daisy the Cow

"Hey diddle diddle,"
Said Daisy the cow.
"I jumped over the moon
But I don't know how.
I made the dog laugh
And the dish ran away.
I think I'll do it again one day."

Cynthia Rider

Grapheme/phoneme correspondence – d

You will need:
coloured pens or pencils

d d d d

d d d d

Katie, a Kitten, and a Kangaroo

Kk

Katie, a Kitten, and a Kangaroo

My friend, Katie,
Went to the zoo.
She came back home
With a kangaroo.
She kept it in the kitchen
With her kitten, Kitty-Sue.
Katie, a kitten,
And a kicking kangaroo!

Cynthia Rider

Grapheme/phoneme correspondence – k

30